G000147090

student WORKBOOK

AQA AS Business Studies
Unit 1: Planning and Financing a Business

John Wolinski and Gwen Coates

Philip Allan Updates, an imprint of Hodder Education, an Hachette UK company, Market Place, Deddington, Oxfordshire, OX15 0SE

Orders
Bookpoint Ltd, 130 Milton Park, Abingdon, Oxfordshire, OX14 4SB
tel: 01235 827827   fax: 01235 400401
e-mail: education@bookpoint.co.uk

Lines are open 9.00 a.m.–5.00 p.m., Monday to Saturday, with a 24-hour message answering service. You can also order through the Philip Allan Updates website: www.philipallan.co.uk

ISBN 978-0-340-97276-2

© Philip Allan Publishers 2008

Printed in Spain

Hachette UK's policy is to use papers that are natural, renewable and recyclable products and made from wood grown in sustainable forests. The logging and manufacturing processes are expected to conform to the environmental regulations of the country of origin.

Introduction

This student workbook is designed to:

- guide you through the content of the new AQA Business Studies AS Unit 1: Planning and Financing a Business
- help you to build your understanding of the two elements of this unit: starting a business; and financial planning
- provide you with a good set of notes on all of the topic areas, to help your revision

For each section of the workbook there is:

- a set of notes providing an overview of the key aspects of the AQA specification
- a variety of questions covering the main topics

Remember that you will be using this workbook to assist your revision as the examination itself approaches, so when answering the questions:

- Use the notes provided in this workbook, but enhance them by using other sources, such as your textbook(s) and notes from class sessions. Remember, the more detailed your answers, the more helpful they will be for your revision.
- Develop your arguments and use the skills that will be required in the examination, such as application, analysis and evaluation.
- Where applicable, use the context of the question (such as the industry or financial situation of the organisation) so that you are demonstrating the vital skill of application.

Progress checklist

Tick the box when you have completed each of the sections below:

Starting a business

Enterprise ☐
Generating and protecting business ideas ☐
Transforming resources into goods and services ☐
Developing business plans ☐
Conducting start-up market research ☐
Understanding markets ☐
Choosing the right legal structure ☐
Raising finance ☐
Locating the business ☐
Employing people ☐

Financial planning

Calculating costs, revenues and profits ☐
Using breakeven analysis to make decisions ☐
Using cash-flow forecasting ☐
Setting budgets ☐
Assessing business start-ups ☐

Starting a business
Enterprise

What is enterprise?

Almost any business or organisation can be called an **enterprise**, but the term usually refers to the process by which new businesses are formed and new products and services are created and brought to the market. Enterprises are usually led by an entrepreneur.

The definition of enterprise capability used by the Department for Children, Schools and Families (DCSF) includes the following skills: innovation, creativity, risk management, risk taking and a can-do attitude.

Individuals who have an idea that they develop by setting up a new business and encouraging it to grow are called **entrepreneurs**. They take the risk and the subsequent profits that come with success or the losses that come with failure.

The characteristics of successful entrepreneurs include:
- determination and persistence
- passion
- the ability to spot and take advantage of opportunities
- relevant skills and expertise
- vision, creativity and innovation
- motivation to succeed and not be daunted by failure
- willingness to take risks — possibly the most important quality of an entrepreneur

The importance of risk and rewards

The majority of new businesses fail for the following reasons:
- lack of finance
- poor infrastructure
- skills shortages
- complexity of regulations or 'red tape'

The ability to evaluate the risks and uncertainty is an integral part of almost all business decisions and an important element of successful entrepreneurship. The outcome of successful risk taking is a profitable venture.

Opportunity cost

Opportunity cost is the 'real cost' of taking a particular action or the next best alternative forgone, i.e. the next best thing that could have been chosen but was not.

Resources, including time and money, are scarce, so choosing to pursue one thing inevitably results in forgoing another thing.

Motives for becoming an entrepreneur

The UK is becoming a more entrepreneurial place and more people are becoming interested in setting up businesses. Possible reasons for this are:
- long-term low interest rates that make it cheaper to borrow money to start a business
- a change in the political climate, so that government supports enterprise and the entrepreneurial spirit
- increasing affluence, which often means that people look for meaning in their lives and one way to do this is to try to fulfil the dream of starting one's own business

Entrepreneurs engage in entrepreneurial activity for a variety of different reasons:
- some to gain more freedom at work
- most to make money
- some to sustain a going concern, such as a family business
- some to provide employment for the local community, sometimes in the form of social enterprises

Government research indicates that a typical entrepreneur in the UK is most likely to be a white man aged around 36 years, who has some form of vocational training or secondary school qualification. He is most likely to be motivated by the freedom that running his own business offers him, or the desire to make money.

Government support for enterprise

The government believes that an environment that encourages enterprise and supports people who take opportunities and risks is crucial for productivity to improve. A strong entrepreneurial base is essential for encouraging growth and prosperity in a modern economy. New and more dynamic businesses increase competitive pressures in markets and facilitate the introduction of new ideas and technologies, and more efficient working practices.

The government has introduced measures to make it easier to start up in business, to run a business and to make a business grow. It has done this by:
- reducing business taxes and trying to establish and maintain a modern and competitive business tax system
- reducing the regulatory burden on enterprises
- reducing barriers to raising finance for small businesses
- improving the support for small and new businesses
- promoting a change in the UK's enterprise culture
- encouraging business start-ups in economically deprived regions of the UK
- introducing legislation to promote competition
- funding projects to raise awareness of enterprise among under-represented groups of people and reviewing how to encourage unemployed people to move into self-employment
- giving financial support to voluntary and not-for-profit organisations that are carrying out excellent work

Questions

1 Explain the following terms:
   a enterprise

   ....

   ....

   ....

   b enterprise skills

   ....

   ....

   ....

   c entrepreneurs

   ....

   ....

   ....

2 Give three examples of successful entrepreneurs.

   ....

   ....

   ....

3 What is a social enterprise? Give two examples.

   ....

   ....

   ....

   ....

4 Outline three characteristics of successful entrepreneurs.

   ....

   ....

   ....

5 Why is the ability to take risks important in developing a successful business?

6 Explain the term 'opportunity cost' and give a business example to illustrate the concept.

7 Suggest two motives for becoming an entrepreneur.

8 Explain why the government wishes to encourage enterprise.

9 Explain three measures introduced by the government to encourage entrepreneurial activity.

10 Give two organisations, other than central government, that provide support for new businesses.

Generating and protecting business ideas

Sources of business ideas

Sources of business ideas include:
- spotting trends and anticipating their impact on people's lives
- identifying a market niche
- copying ideas from other countries — many entrepreneurs have found and copied successful ideas from abroad
- taking a scientific approach — entrepreneurs sometimes work in a laboratory or university to invent original new products

Franchising

Franchising is when the owner of a business (the franchisor) grants a licence to another person or business (the franchisee) to use their business idea — often in a specific geographical area.

Benefits of operating as a franchise are:
- Franchises offer the least amount of risk for a start-up.
- Franchise businesses usually have established brand names.
- As a result of the above, financing the business may be easier.
- The franchisee is likely to incur lower advertising and promotional costs, as the business is likely to benefit from national campaigns by the franchisor.
- The franchisee usually has exclusive rights in its area.
- Relationships with suppliers may have been established by the franchisor.
- The franchisor often offers support and training.

Possible pitfalls of operating as a franchise include:
- The franchisor may not have researched the business carefully.
- Costs may be higher than expected.
- Ongoing royalties and other payments may have to be paid to the franchisor.
- Other franchisees may give the brand a bad reputation.
- The franchise agreement usually includes restrictions on how the business should be run.
- Franchisees are required to sign non-competition clauses.
- As franchisees must be approved by the franchisor, an existing franchisee may find it difficult to sell the franchise.
- If the franchisor goes out of business or changes the way it does things, this will have a direct impact on the franchisee's business.

Protecting a business idea

There are three main ways of protecting a business idea:
- **copyright** — legal protection against copying for authors, composers and artists
- **patent** — an official document granting the holder the right to be the only user or producer of a newly invented product or process for a specified period
- **trademark** — a sign, logo, symbol or words displayed on a company's products or on its advertising, including sounds or music, which distinguishes its brands from those of its competitors

Questions

1 Use three different business examples to illustrate three possible sources of business opportunities.

2 What is a franchise?

3 Rhona is thinking of setting up a hairdressing business but is unsure whether to apply for a franchise or to set up as an independent business. Outline two possible benefits to the business of operating a franchise compared to starting a new business.

4 Outline two problems that Rhona might encounter as a result of operating a franchise compared to starting a new business.

5 Explain the meaning of the term 'copyright'.

6 How might copyright benefit authors or musicians?

7 What is a patent?

8 What is a trademark and why might it benefit a business?

9 Discuss whether ownership of a patent is likely to be beneficial for an entrepreneur with an original business idea.

10 To what extent might the level of risk and the potential to grow differ for an entrepreneur, like Rhona, if she decides to develop her hairdressing business via a franchise rather than setting up as an independent business?

Transforming resources into goods and services

Resources

In order to produce goods and services, a business will need to use resources. These resources are the **inputs** into the production process, but are more commonly known as the **factors of production**. They are:

- **land** — all the natural resources that can be used for production, including land itself, but also natural and mineral resources (e.g. oil) and animals (e.g. cows, fish)
- **labour** — both the physical and mental effort involved in production
- **capital** — goods that are made in order to produce other goods and services (e.g. factories, machinery, lorries)
- **enterprise** — bringing together the factors of production to create goods and services

Outputs

The **outputs** of the production process can be classified according to the different sectors of industry, as shown in the following table.

Classification of outputs

Industry sector	Type of output
Primary industries	Natural resources
Secondary industries	Manufactured goods
Tertiary industries	Services

The process whereby resources are converted into goods or services that satisfy the customers is known as **production** or the **transformation process**.

The transformation process

The purpose of a business is to produce goods or services, usually in order to generate profits. To achieve this, a business must acquire inputs, convert them into outputs, and ensure that they reach the customer. All of these activities are part of the transformation process.

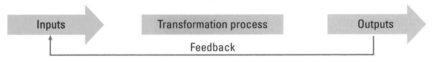

The transformation process

The various inputs are affected differently by the transformation process:

- Generally, **labour** and **enterprise** are unaffected by the transformation process and can be used repeatedly.
- **Capital** can be used many times, although it does eventually wear out (depreciate).
- **Land**, in the form of natural resources, is used up in the transformation process. Thus many businesses look to recycle or minimise the use of these scarce resources.

Adding value

Adding value is the process of increasing the worth of resources by modifying them.
The transformation process is a major factor in adding value. For example, the value of the
components used to make a car is much less than the value of the finished car.

The level of added value can be calculated using the following formula:

added value = sales revenue – the cost of bought-in materials, components and services

Improving the efficiency of factors of production can help to add value. Examples are:
- increasing the level of investment in capital equipment
- using renewable or recyclable resources
- training workers
- improving the fertility of land
- encouraging entrepreneurs and risk taking

A business can also add value by getting customers to pay higher prices or buy more. This could
be achieved by:
- producing high-quality products
- offering good after-sales service
- using marketing to persuade customers to buy more and/or pay higher prices

Questions

1 Define the term 'adding value'.

....

....

2 The table below shows the transformation process of a product that undergoes six different stages
of production. Complete the table to show how much value is added at each stage and the value at
the end of each stage.

Stage of production/ transformation	Value at beginning of stage (£)	Value added (£)	Value at end of stage (£)
1 Components purchased	20	0	
2 Framework assembled	20		30
3 Basic product completed	30	15	
4 Extra features added			75
5 Product transported to shop	75	12	
6 Shop displays and sells product			125

3 Analyse two possible reasons why stage 6 adds most value to many products.

....

....

....

....

4 Analyse three different ways in which a farmer might be able to increase his value added by improving the effectiveness of his factors of production.

....

....

....

....

....

....

....

5 Identify the four factors of production.

....

6 Label the diagram to show the four stages of the transformation process.

7 Identify one example for each of these:
   a a business that uses a relatively high level of **labour** in its transformation (production) process

....

   b a business that uses a relatively high level of **land** in its transformation process

....

   c a business that uses a relatively high level of **capital** in its transformation process

....

Developing business plans

Purpose of a business plan

A **business plan** is a report describing the marketing strategy, operational issues and financial implications of a business start-up. It offers the following benefits:

- It is useful in helping entrepreneurs clarify their objectives.
- It enables owners to know precisely what needs to be done to meet their business objectives.
- It is an essential document in persuading lenders to invest capital in the business.
- If reviewed and updated regularly, it can be a valuable tool in running the business.
- An accurate and realistic plan will identify the business's strengths and opportunities as well as its weaknesses and possible threats.

Content of a business plan

The business plan should contain:

- details about the business, including its name and location, its legal structure and a description of its product or service
- personal information about the owner and managers, details of any support they are receiving, and details of key staff and staffing requirements
- the objectives of the firm, stated as quantifiable or SMART targets
- a marketing plan
- a production plan
- details of fixed assets, including how these are to be financed
- a sales and cash-flow forecast, a projected profit and loss account, a balance sheet for the next 2–3 years, details of pricing and breakeven level
- details of the finance needed from the lender or investor and the forecast speed of repayment or rate of return on the investor's capital
- the collateral to be offered
- a brief account of the long-term forecasts and plans of the business
- a SWOT analysis

Sources of information and guidance

Most entrepreneurs do not have the skills necessary both to plan and to run a business, and need to seek specialist advice on a range of issues.

- Accountants and bank managers provide advice on how to manage a business financially.
- Business Link is a government-funded service that provides the information, advice and support needed to start, maintain and grow a business.
- Other sources of advice and support include local enterprise agencies, chambers of commerce and local trade associations.
- For entrepreneurs aged 18–30, the Prince's Trust offers help and, often, funding, while at the other end of the age range, PRIME helps the over-fifties.
- Individual advisers, specialising in small businesses, can provide guidance and support.

Questions

1 What is a business plan?

....

....

2 Taki is thinking of setting up a new computer business that would involve him in building, selling and maintaining computers for personal rather than commercial customers. Explain how a business plan might be of benefit to him in this venture.

....

....

....

....

3 Why might an over-optimistic business plan lead to problems for Taki and his potential computer business?

....

....

....

....

....

4 Outline the type of information that should be included in the marketing section of Taki's business plan.

....

....

....

5 Outline the type of information that should be included in the production section of Taki's business plan.

....

....

....

6 Outline the type of information that should be included in the finance section of Taki's business plan.

....

7 Outline the type of information that should be included in the personal and staffing section of Taki's business plan.

8 Apart from marketing, production, finance and personnel, identify two other areas of information that a business plan might include.

9 Identify the various sources of advice and information available for a start-up business and analyse why such advice and information might be necessary.

10 To what extent might a business plan improve the possibility of success for Taki's potential computer business as well as helping to maintain that success?

Conducting start-up market research

What is market research?

Market research is the systematic and objective collection, analysis and evaluation of information that is intended to assist the marketing process.

Marketing is the process of anticipating and satisfying customers' wants in a way that delights the customer and also meets the needs of the organisation.

There are two main types of market research:
- **primary market research** — the collection of information first-hand for a specific purpose
- **secondary market research** — the use of information that has already been collected for a different purpose

Primary market research

The main methods of conducting primary research are as follows:
- **Experiments and/or observations** — looking at how customers react in certain situations. Experiments have the advantage of observing actual customer behaviour, but they may not reveal *why* customers behave in a certain way and they can be expensive.
- **Focus groups** — a group of consumers is encouraged to discuss, in detail, their feelings about a product or market. This method helps a firm to gather in-depth details on consumers, but the group may be biased and focus groups are expensive to operate.
- **Surveys.** The main types of survey are:
  - **Personal interviews** — these gather a wide range of information, but they can be time consuming and the answers and/or sample may be biased.
  - **Postal surveys** — these are cheap, good for targeting geographical areas, and can be quite detailed, but response rates are usually low and the replies are often biased.
  - **Telephone interviews** — telephone calls are cheap and can be targeted directly, but detailed questions are impossible and phone interviews are often unpopular.
  - **Internet surveys** — questionnaires on internet sites enable customers to express their views, thus giving valuable information to the website owner. They are cheap and good for targeting, but the sample will tend to be biased.

Secondary market research

Secondary information is found by examining published documents (i.e. through desk research). Some main examples are:
- government publications
- newspapers and magazines
- company records and publications
- competitors' materials
- the internet

The main benefits of secondary market research are:
- The information is already available.
- It is cheaper than primary research.
- Secondary surveys are often conducted regularly, so trends over time can be identified.

Drawbacks of secondary market research are:
- The information may be dated.
- The data are also available to other firms.
- The secondary user may not know the level of accuracy and reliability of the data.

Qualitative market research

Qualitative market research is the collection of information about the market based on subjective factors such as opinions and reasons.

The benefits of qualitative market research are:
- A business can use it to get a better idea of how to appeal to its consumers.
- It helps to shape marketing approaches by finding out why people buy products.

The problems are:
- It is very expensive to gather.
- It tends to be small scale and thus possibly biased.

Quantitative market research

Quantitative market research is the collection of information about the market based on numbers.

The benefits of quantitative market research are:
- It summarises data in a concise and meaningful way.
- The use of numerical data makes it easier to compare results with other organisations.
- Numerical data can be used to identify trends and project future trends.

The problems are:
- It only shows 'what', rather than explaining 'why'.
- It can lack reliability and validity if the sample is biased or too small.

Sampling

A **sample** is a group of respondents or factors whose views or behaviour should be representative of the target market as a whole.

Primary market research is undertaken by sampling the views of a small selection of consumers. The **sample size** is the number of people or items in the sample. Large samples increase reliability but cost more. Small samples decrease costs but are less reliable.

There are three main types of sample:
- **Random sample** — a group of respondents in which each member of the target population has an equal chance of being chosen.
- **Quota sample** — a group of respondents comprising several different segments, each sharing a common feature (e.g. age, gender). The number of interviewees is fixed to reflect their percentage of the total, but interviewees are selected non-randomly by the interviewer.

- **Stratified sample** — a group of respondents selected according to particular features (e.g. age, gender). However, unlike quota sampling, where the final selection is left to an interviewer, in stratified sampling the sub-groups and their sizes are chosen specifically.

The problems of sampling, in general, are:
- Samples may be unrepresentative (e.g. asking the wrong people).
- There may be bias in questions or in the answers that they encourage.
- It may be difficult to locate suitable respondents.

Several factors influence which sampling method is chosen:
- costs and the availability of finance
- time
- whether the business is targeting a specific group of customers
- the firm's understanding of its customer base

Questions

1 What is the difference between qualitative market research and quantitative market research?

....
....
....

2 Jackie is opening a new computer repair shop. She is thinking of using an internet survey or a personal survey. Advise her on her best choice, giving reasons for your recommendation.

....
....
....
....

3 Phil is thinking of opening a restaurant and wants to know two things:
- what people like to eat in his town
- how many customers he is likely to get

Analyse two different types of market research that Phil should use to discover this information.

....
....
....
....
....

4 Explain two benefits of using secondary market research rather than primary market research.

....

....

....

....

5 Explain two reasons why Phil might use random sampling for his restaurant.

....

....

....

....

6 Analyse two reasons why a national chain of restaurants might prefer to use quota sampling rather than random sampling.

....

....

....

....

7 Evaluate the main factors that Jackie would need to consider in deciding on her sample size and her sampling method, in order to carry out market research for her computer repair shop.

....

....

....

....

....

....

....

....

....

Understanding markets

What is a market?

A **market** is a place where buyers and sellers come together.

Markets can be classified in different ways.

Geographical classification:
- **Local markets.** These serve a limited geographic area, close to where customers live.
- **National markets.** Many industrial and primary products are sold on a national scale.

Physical and non-physical markets:
- **Physical markets.** In a physical market there is an actual place where buyers and sellers meet, such as a shop.
- **Electronic/non-physical markets.** Telephone sales and the internet are now often used to bring buyers and sellers together.

Demand

Demand is the amount of a product or service that consumers are willing and able to buy at any given price over a period of time.

The major factors that influence demand are:
- **Price.** As the price of a product rises, the demand for it will usually fall, and vice versa. For products with close substitutes, price changes have a major impact on the quantity demanded. For necessities, however, demand does not vary much, even if price changes.
- **Income and wealth.** The demand for a product is influenced by the ability to purchase it, so this is a very important factor.
- **Tastes and fashion.** This is a crucial influence on demand for items such as clothing and entertainment.
- **Substitute products.** Demand for a product may decline because a competitor's alternative becomes more popular, perhaps through a cut in its price.
- **Complementary products.** These products are used alongside each other, such as chicken tikka masala and pilau rice. If the demand for chicken tikka masala increases, this may lead to more demand for pilau rice.
- **Seasonal factors.** Many products, such as suntan cream, are bought more frequently at certain times of the year.
- **Demographic factors.** Population changes can influence the numbers and types of products bought.
- **Marketing and advertising.** Successful marketing can increase demand for a good.

Market segmentation

Market segmentation is the classification of customers or potential customers into groups or sub-groups (market segments), each of which responds differently to different products or marketing approaches.

Types of market segmentation are:
- age
- gender (sex)
- social class
- geographic
- lifestyle
- usage/frequency of purchase

Market segmentation helps a business to get to know its customers (or potential customers) and their preferences. This enables it to:
- increase market share, by adapting its marketing to customers' interests
- know which new products to develop, by concentrating on serving the needs of customers who are most likely to increase their buying
- extend products into new markets, by identifying market segments that may be interested in the product but which have not yet been reached
- improve marketing by using messages and media that will excite the target market

Problems with market segmentation are:
- difficulty in identifying the most important segments for a product — who will be most interested in the product?
- knowing how to reach the chosen segment — what media do they read or watch?
- recognising changes in the relevant segments — are their interests changing?
- ignoring the needs of customers not included in the chosen segment — there may be a lot of unsatisfied demand if the product is not aimed at certain market segments

Market size, growth and share

Market size is the volume of sales of a product (e.g. the number of computers sold) or the value of sales of a product (e.g. the total revenue from computer sales).

Market growth is the percentage change in sales (volume or value) over a period.

Market share is the percentage or proportion of the total sales of a product or service achieved by a firm or a specific brand of a product.

Market share is usually measured as a percentage, calculated by the formula:

$$\text{market share} = \frac{\text{sales of one product or brand or company}}{\text{total sales in the market}} \times 100$$

Questions

1 What is meant by 'a market'?

....

....

2 Explain why most consumer products are sold in 'local markets'.

3 Examine two reasons for the growth of 'non-physical' markets in recent years.

4 List six factors that might influence the demand for a good or service.

5 Choose a product that has benefited from increased demand recently. Evaluate the main reasons for this increase in demand, emphasising the reasons why some factors have been more important than others.

6 Ali has just opened a nightclub. What are the main market segments that she should target? Justify your choices.

....

....

....

....

7 Explain two problems that Ali might experience in using market segmentation.

....

....

....

....

8 Evaluate how Ali's understanding of her market segments might help her in her marketing.

....

....

....

....

....

....

....

....

....

9 Tables 1 and 2 show data about nightclubs in Ali's hometown, during 2009.

Table 1 Nightclub attendances, 2009

Nightclub	Number of customers per week	Market share (%)
Ali's	450	
Guy and Toni's	750	
St Elmo's Fire	1,200	40
Stephen Fry experience	600	20
All nightclubs		

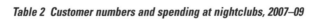

Table 2 Customer numbers and spending at nightclubs, 2007–09

	2007	2008	2009
Sales volume (customer numbers)	2,600	2,200	3,000
Sales value (revenue received)	£52,000	£48,400	£63,000

a Insert the missing figures in Table 1.

b Calculate the percentage growth in the volume of nightclub customers between 2007 and 2009 (to 1 decimal place).

c Calculate the percentage growth in the value of nightclub customers between 2007 and 2009 (to 1 decimal place).

d What happened to the amount paid per customer between 2007 and 2009?

10 How might Ali use these data to help her nightclub become more popular?

Choosing the right legal structure

Unincorporated and incorporated businesses

In an **unincorporated business**, there is no distinction in law between the individual owner and the business itself. The identity of the business and the owner is the same. Such businesses tend to be sole traders or partnerships.

The legal identify of an **incorporated business** is separate from the individual owners. As a result, these organisations can own assets, owe money and enter into contracts in their own right. Such businesses include private limited companies and public limited companies.

Limited and unlimited liability

Unlimited liability means the owners of a business are liable for all the debts of the business. Unlimited liability is a characteristic of businesses that are unincorporated. If the debts of the business are greater than the personal assets of the owners, they may be forced into bankruptcy.

Limited liability means the liability of the owners of a business is limited to the fully paid-up value of the share capital. Limited liability is a feature of incorporated businesses. Limiting the amount of shareholders' liability is an important factor in encouraging people to invest.

Types of legal structure

- **Sole trader** — a business owned by one person. The owner may employ other people.
- **Partnership** — a form of business in which two or more people operate for the common goal of making a profit. The Partnership Act (1890) forms the basis of partnership law in the UK. Under the Limited Partnership Act (1907), a **limited partnership** can be formed when at least one partner assumes responsibility for managing and running the business and has unlimited liability, and at least one partner contributes finance but has no involvement in the management or running of the business. The Limited Liability Partnership Act (2000) introduced the **limited liability partnership** (LLP) in response to concern about the unlimited liability of partners for very large legal claims, particularly for professional negligence. The LLP enables partners who are actively involved in the business to limit their liability for debts.
- **Private limited company** — a small to medium-sized business run by the family or small group of individuals who own it. A private limited company can keep its affairs reasonably private, its shares cannot be traded on the Stock Exchange and it must have 'Ltd' in its name.
- **Public limited company** — a business with limited liability, a share capital of over £50,000, at least two shareholders, two directors and a qualified company secretary, and usually a wide spread of shareholders. The shares of public limited companies are traded on the Stock Exchange, which enables these businesses to raise finance more easily. Public limited companies must have 'plc' after the company name.

The motive for changing from a private to a public limited company is usually to obtain extra funds for growth, but disadvantages include:
- loss of control
- continual scrutiny
- short-termism regarding share prices and possibly takeover pressure

The divorce of ownership and control

Traditionally, entrepreneurs have two functions:
- **ownership** — providing finance and therefore taking risks
- **control** — managing the organisation and making decisions

In a sole trader business, the owner and manager are likely to be the same person, so these functions remain with the entrepreneur. In public limited companies, the owners (shareholders) vote for a board of directors, who in turn appoint managers to control and manage the business. In this case, the two functions of ownership and control are separated or 'divorced', which may create problems if owners have different objectives from those in control.

Not-for-profit organisations

This sector includes voluntary and community organisations, charities, social enterprises, pressure groups, cooperatives, mutual societies and trusts. Although the organisations vary, they share the following characteristics:
- They are non-governmental organisations.
- They have a governing body responsible for managing their affairs.
- They tend to have social or environmental aims and objectives.
- They are usually established for purposes other than financial gain.
- Many use volunteer staff in addition to paid employees.

Factors affecting the choice of legal structure

The choice of legal structure is determined by:
- the size of the business, and the level and type of investment required
- the need for limited liability
- the degree of control desired by the original owners
- the nature of the business and the level of risk involved

Questions

1 a What is meant by the term 'incorporated business'?

b Which two legal structures are likely to be incorporated businesses?

2 a What is meant by the term 'unincorporated business'?

b Which two legal structures are likely to be unincorporated businesses?

3 What are the implications for a business if its owners have unlimited liability?

4 What are the implications for a business if its owners have limited liability?

5 Simon has just completed an apprenticeship as a plumber and is planning to set up his own business. Give two advantages and two disadvantages of setting up his business as a sole trader rather than a partnership.

6 Explain the difference between a limited liability partnership and an ordinary partnership.

7 Distinguish between a private limited company and a public limited company.

8 Outline two advantages and two disadvantages of a private limited company over a public limited company.

9 Analyse the factors that can influence the most appropriate legal structure that a business should adopt.

10 Discuss the factors that companies such as Pizza Express, New Look and Esporta might have taken into account when making the decision to change from being a public limited company to becoming a private limited company.

Raising finance

Methods of raising finance

The main ways of raising finance for a start-up business are:
- ordinary share capital
- loan capital (e.g. bank loan)
- bank overdraft
- venture capital
- personal sources

In addition, it may be possible to get help via the government.

Ordinary share capital is money given to a company by shareholders in return for a share certificate. This gives the shareholder part ownership of the company and entitles them to a share of the profits.

Features of ordinary share capital include the following:
- Shareholders usually receive one vote for each share that they own.
- The shareholders themselves decide at the annual general meeting what dividend per share will be paid, but there is no guaranteed level of dividend.
- Ordinary share capital appeals to investors who are prepared to take a risk in return for (usually) higher rewards.
- In the event of liquidation, shareholders are protected by limited liability. They can only lose the paid-up value of their shares and cannot be asked to pay any more money.
- Ordinary shares are often known as permanent capital, as the business will always have shareholders who own these shares.
- If a person wants to sell shares, they must find a buyer. This is usually done through the stock market, which deals mainly in second-hand shares of public limited companies.

Loan capital is money received by an organisation in return for the organisation's agreement to pay interest during the period of the loan and to repay the loan within an agreed time.

A **bank loan** is a sum of money provided to a firm or an individual by a bank for a specific, agreed purpose. The terms of a bank loan usually specify the purpose, the interest rates, repayment dates and any collateral (security) needed. The size of the loan may be limited by the security offered.

Bank overdrafts occur when a bank allows an individual or organisation to overspend its current account in the bank up to an agreed (overdraft) limit and for a stated time period.

Venture capital is finance provided to small or medium-sized firms that seek growth, but which may be considered risky by typical share buyers or other lenders. It commonly involves sums of between £50,000 and £100,000. Investors may also offer business advice.

Personal sources of finance describe money that is provided by the owners of the business from their own savings or personal wealth. If no borrowing is involved, these can be cheap sources of money. For small business start-ups, such as sole traders or partnerships, this is often the most practical way of raising finance for a new business.

The main sources of personal finance are as follows:
- personal savings accumulated before the business commenced
- a mortgage on a property
- borrowing privately from friends and family
- selling private assets

It is possible for some start-ups to get government help in raising finance through the small firms loan guarantee and community development finance institutions (CDFIs).

Capital expenditure and revenue expenditure

When considering sources of finance, the most critical factor is the length of time for which the finance is needed. Finance is used to fund:
- **Capital expenditure** — spending on items that can be used repeatedly (fixed assets). It may take a long time for these items to generate enough revenue to pay for themselves, so a long-term source of finance is best.
- **Revenue expenditure** — spending on current, day-to-day costs, such as the purchase of raw materials and payment of wages. Such expenditure provides a quick return, so the company should rely on a short-term source of finance.

The following table classifies the main sources of finance in terms of the usual time period.

Sources of finance classified by time period

Long-term finance	Medium-term finance	Short-term finance
Personal sources	Personal sources	Personal sources
Ordinary share capital		
Loan capital/ bank loan	Loan capital/ bank loan	
		Bank overdraft
Venture capital	Venture capital	
Government help	Government help	

Factors influencing how finance is raised

The way in which finance is raised is influenced by several factors:

- **Legal structure of the business.** Private limited companies and public limited companies will sell shares; sole traders and partnerships will rely on personal finance.
- **Use of the finance.** The basic rule is that the length of time that it takes a business to earn the money should match the length of time a business has to repay the money.
- **Amount required.** The larger the sum, the less likely it is that the owner(s) will be able to generate enough finance from internal sources.
- **Level of risk.** If an enterprise is viewed as risky, firms will find it harder to attract loans, although venture capital may be a possibility.
- **Views of the owners.** Shareholders or owners may be reluctant to lose control of a firm, so they may reject shares and venture capital, for reasons of control.

Questions

1 What is meant by the following terms?

  a ordinary share capital

  b venture capital

  c personal sources of finance

2 What is the difference between a bank loan and a bank overdraft?

3 Complete the following table by explaining **one** advantage and **one** disadvantage of each method of raising finance.

Method of raising finance	Advantage	Disadvantage
Ordinary share capital		
Venture capital		
Personal sources		
Bank loan		
Bank overdraft		

4 Classify each of the following items of expenditure as **either** capital expenditure **or** revenue expenditure. Delete as appropriate.

a buying a machine	capital/revenue
b paying wages	capital/revenue
c buying raw materials	capital/revenue
d building a factory	capital/revenue
e purchasing a vehicle	capital/revenue
f marketing expenditure	capital/revenue

5 Of the five ways of raising finance mentioned in questions 1 and 2, which **one** should only ever be used as a form of:

a long-term finance

....

....

....

b short-term finance

....

....

....

Explain the reasons for your choices.

6 The table below lists five business situations. For each situation, select one of the following ways to raise finance and justify your choice:

- ordinary share capital
- bank overdraft
- personal sources
- loan capital (e.g. bank loan)
- venture capital

Situation	Recommended way of raising finance	Reasons for your choice
a A taxi company wants to buy a new taxi which should pay for itself after 4 years.		
b A start-up owner wants to be independent. She has high levels of savings. Interest rates are quite high.		
c A sole trader business has seasonal sales and his customers expect to be given 90 days to pay for their purchases.		
d A newly formed private limited company wants to develop a new invention. It is unlikely to make much profit for a few years but is then expected to make a lot of profit. The current owners do not have very much money.		
e A small limited company wants to develop an idea that is risky. The owners feel that they might need some advice on marketing.		

Locating the business

Factors

The main factors influencing location of business start-ups are:
- technology
- costs
- infrastructure
- the market
- qualitative factors

Technology

Communication technologies, such as mobile phones and the internet, make it much easier for entrepreneurs to work from home or away from a centralised base.

Teleworking involves working in a location that is separate from a central workplace, using telecommunication technologies to enable this to take place.

The three main reasons for operating a business from home are:
- low cost
- flexibility, enabling staff to work outside normal office hours
- easier growth

Manufacturing businesses that use technological equipment often need to locate on industrial estates or factory premises.

Costs

Often firms will locate at the **least-cost site** — the business location that allows a firm to minimise its costs.

The main costs to consider are land (rent); labour costs/labour cost per unit produced; transport costs — for both raw materials/supplies and finished products.

Infrastructure

Infrastructure is the network of utilities, such as transport links, sewerage, telecommunications systems, health services and educational facilities.

For small businesses, the local infrastructure may be more important than the national infrastructure. The following questions would be of particular significance to a small business.
- Are parking spaces available nearby?
- How much does it cost to park?
- Is traffic flow good?
- Is it on a bus route or close to a station?
- If the business is a shop, is it isolated or convenient for visits to other shops?
- Is it easy to receive deliveries?

The market

For retailers and other service industries, the market is the most important influence on location. As the UK's economy is predominantly based on tertiary production (the provision of services), this makes the market a crucial factor in determining the location of many UK firms. Organisations save transport costs if they locate close to their market.

Qualitative factors

Ultimately, all business decisions are taken by individuals. Owners may include personal opinions in their choice of location. Examples are locating:

- near the owner's home
- in a place that may attract customers rather than save costs
- in pleasant surroundings
- close to amenities such as shops

Locating small businesses

Research into the location of small firms identified the following key factors that a small firm should consider:

- demographic factors (e.g. whether the local population matches the target market)
- the economic wealth of the local area and whether it could support the number of businesses located in the vicinity
- pedestrian traffic flow (footfall) during opening times
- parking factors — cost and time
- competitors' locations — is competition fierce?
- location history — does the site have a good track record of successful business activity?
- council policies, such as limiting certain business activities (e.g. nightclubs) to certain areas

Questions

1 Why is teleworking so popular with small start-ups?

2 Explain one reason why a newsagent would want to locate at the least-cost site and one reason why it might *not* want to locate at the least-cost site.

3 Analyse two ways in which infrastructure might influence the location of a small textile manufacturer.

....

....

....

....

....

4 Why might firms in the tertiary sector, such as restaurants, be more likely to locate close to the market than firms in the primary sector, such as farmers?

....

....

....

....

....

5 Identify four qualitative factors that might influence the location of a business.

....

....

....

....

6 Look at the table below. Kim is planning to set up a hairdressing and beauty salon, aimed at 20–30-year-olds with above average incomes. She has identified three alternative locations that are briefly described in the table.

Feature	Locations		
	Allen Avenue	**Carty Close**	**Star Street**
Footfall: passers-by per hour	200	120	90
Parking spaces nearby	1,000	300	60
Parking costs (per hour)	£1.00	£0.50	Free
Number of competitors within 200 metres	5	1	0
% of people aged 20–30	15	20	25
% with above average incomes	80	30	60

In which one of these three locations would you recommend Kim to set up her new hairdressing and beauty salon? Justify your decision.

Employing people

Why do businesses employ people?

There are several reasons for employing people.

- Only in the smallest businesses will the owner have the capacity to carry out all the tasks necessary to provide the finished product or service.
- Most businesses need specialist expertise to make their products, to market them and to manage their finances.
- Some businesses are seasonal in nature; the demand for their products will peak at certain times of the year and drop away at other times.
- A start-up business that wants to expand will need to consider outsourcing, training existing staff or taking on new staff.

Employees in small businesses

Decisions on the types of employee to use in a small business will depend on how constant the work is, how long the work will last and the number of hours of work required each week. Contractually, the following options are available:

- permanent employees, who can be full time or part time
- temporary or fixed-term employees
- zero-hours contractors
- employment agency staff
- self-employed freelancers, consultants and contractors

Permanent or temporary staff?

Staff who are required throughout the year and whose services are necessary to the continued running of the business are likely to be permanent employees. They include management, factory operatives, sales assistants and administrative staff. Permanent staff tend to be more loyal to the business and more motivated then temporary staff, who have less allegiance and less commitment to the business. Where additional staff are needed — for example, to meet the seasonal demand for goods or services, to complete a particular task or to cover a particular event such as maternity leave — they are more likely to be employed on a temporary basis.

Full-time or part-time staff?

This depends on the nature of the job and the needs of the business, but also on the individual employee. Some jobs clearly need to be full time, such as a machine operator in a factory or a telephonist, but others, such as a cleaner, might require just a few hours per week. A business could also introduce job sharing, where two or more people share the responsibilities, pay and benefits of a full-time job in proportion to the hours they work. This is a way of retaining staff who can no longer work full time and may otherwise wish to leave.

Employing part-time workers might help a firm by:

- keeping costs down

- building in flexibility and allowing the business to respond to change
- increasing motivation, reducing stress and raising productivity
- attracting a wider pool of candidates for vacancies
- enabling it to retain employees

However, employing people has the following drawbacks:
- meeting the range of employment legislation requirements
- managing staff
- employee absence
- higher costs as a result of extra induction, training and administration

External consultants, contractors and advisers

In addition to employees, a business might hire the services of consultants, contractors and advisers. As these people will be self-employed or belong to a separate company, this is a useful way of taking advantage of extra skills and labour without taking on many of the responsibilities of an employer. Other advisers, such as Business Link and Prince's Trust mentors, provide their services free to start-up businesses.

Questions

1 Explain the reasons why a small business might need to employ people.

2 Of the following statements, which two are correct? Write your answers here: ....
  A Permanent employees can be full-time or part-time employees.
  B Temporary employees cannot be full-time employees.
  C Part-time employees are always temporary employees.
  D Full-time employees can be permanent or temporary employees.

3 Under what circumstances might a business decide to employ people on a permanent rather than a temporary basis? Give examples to illustrate your answer.

4 Outline two advantages of employing people on a temporary rather than a permanent basis. Give examples to illustrate your answer.

5 Analyse the advantages to a business of providing the opportunity for more of its staff to work part time.

6 What is a zero-hours employment contract?

7 Outline the benefits and drawbacks to a business of using employment agency staff.

8 Rashida is a sole trader who runs a small laundry business from a workshop on an industrial estate. She collects, launders, irons and delivers the clothes. Consider the advantages that might result if she decides to employ people in her business.

9 Consider the drawbacks and difficulties she is likely to encounter if she employs people in her business.

....

....

....

....

....

....

....

10 A small training business has, unexpectedly, gained a lot of new work. Much of it is in areas in which the business has high levels of expertise but insufficient staff to fulfil the demand. Some of it is in areas where it has little or no expertise. It does not want to turn this additional business down. Evaluate the benefits to the business of hiring external consultants rather than employing more temporary staff.

....

....

....

....

....

....

....

....

....

....

Financial planning
Calculating costs, revenues and profits

Price, total revenue and profit

Price is the amount paid by a consumer to purchase 1 unit of a product.

A business must set a price that is high enough to cover the costs of making a product and leave a profit. However, if the price is too high, fewer customers are likely to buy the product.

The business must find the ideal selling price — the one that helps the firm to reach its financial targets, such as making high levels of profit.

Total revenue, or sales revenue, is the **income** received from an organisation's activities. It can be calculated by multiplying the average selling price by the quantity sold:

> total revenue = price per unit × quantity of units sold

For example, if the selling price is £42 and 2,000 items are sold, total revenue is £84,000.

Profit is the difference between the income of a business and its total costs.

> profit = total revenue – total costs

Profit is often the main objective of a business. Two ways of improving profit are to:
- increase sales revenue
- decrease costs

Costs

Cutting costs may help a firm to increase its profit, as long as the cuts do not reduce the attractiveness of the good or service and make customers less likely to buy the products.

Costs can be classified into fixed and variable costs.
- **Fixed costs** are costs that do not vary directly with output in the short run. Examples include machinery, rent and rates, salaries, administration, vehicles, marketing, and lighting and heating.
- **Variable costs** are costs that vary directly with output in the short run. Examples include raw materials, wages of operatives/direct labour, and power to run the machinery.

Total cost is the sum of fixed costs and variable costs.

If there is a 5% rise in output, it is assumed that:
- fixed costs do not change
- variable costs rise by 5% (because variable costs per unit stay the same)

The following table shows the effect of changes in output on costs for a product which has fixed costs of £120 and variable costs of £4 per unit.

Units of output	Fixed costs (£)	Total variable costs (£)	Total costs (£)	Average (unit) costs (£)
0	120	0	120	–
10	120	40	160	16
20	120	80	200	10
30	120	120	240	8
40	120	160	280	7

The relationship between cost and price

If costs are generally rising, a firm has two main options:
- Increase the price of its finished product by a similar amount to the cost increase. This will enable it to keep its **profit margin** (the difference between the selling price of an item and the cost of making or buying that item) on each product that it sells. This higher price may lead to a fall in demand. However, demand may not fall if every business is increasing its prices because of similar cost increases.
- Keep the price unchanged and 'absorb' the cost increase. This will reduce the profit margin on each item but may increase profit *if* there is a large increase in demand because of this strategy.

Questions

1 State three fixed costs for a restaurant.

....

....

....

2 Identify two variable costs for a restaurant.

....

....

3 Calculate the total revenue if the price per unit is £6 and 42,000 units are sold.

....

4 A business sets itself a target to achieve sales revenue of £38,500 from a product that is sold for £22. How many units does it need to sell to reach its target sales revenue?

....

5 Complete Table 1 based on the following data for Radfast Ltd:
- fixed costs = £4,000
- variable costs = £4 per unit
- selling price = £6 per unit

Table 1 Initial financial data for Radfast Ltd

Units of output	Total revenue	Fixed costs	Variable costs	Total costs	Profit
0					
1,000					
2,000					
3,000					
4,000					
5,000					

6 Radfast Ltd is thinking of introducing new technology in order to replace some of its workers. As a consequence, the selling price of the product stays at £6 per unit, but the costs change to the figures set out below:
- fixed costs = £12,000
- variable costs = £2 per unit

a Briefly explain why introducing new technology in order to replace some workers will lead to these changes in fixed costs and variable costs.

....

....

....

b Complete the following table, based on the new costs but with the selling price unchanged at £6.

Table 2 New financial data for Radfast Ltd

Units of output	Total revenue	Fixed costs	Variable costs	Total costs	Profit
0					
1,000					
2,000					
3,000					
4,000					
5,000					

7 Using the figures in Tables 1 and 2, and any other reasons that you think are relevant, advise Radfast Ltd on whether it should replace workers with new technology. Justify your view.

Using breakeven analysis to make decisions

Contribution

Contribution shows whether a product is helping the business to make a profit.

All firms need to pay their fixed costs in order to operate. These costs must be covered before a profit can be made. Contribution ignores these fixed costs. Instead it looks only at the variable costs. If the sales revenue from making the product is greater than the variable costs, the product is contributing towards paying off the fixed costs or making a profit.

    contribution per unit = selling price per unit – variable cost per unit

The **total contribution** of a product can be calculated in two ways:

    total contribution = contribution per unit × no. of units sold

    total contribution = total revenue – total variable costs

If total contribution exceeds fixed costs, the business will be making a profit.

Calculating contribution per unit and total contribution

A businessman opens a souvenir shop. His estimates for revenue and costs are set out below:
- fixed costs (per year) = £24,000
- variable costs = £8 per souvenir
- selling price = £20 per souvenir
- no. of souvenirs sold per year = 3,200

The contribution per unit = £20 – £8 = £12.

Using the first of the two formulae above:

    total contribution = £12 × 3,200 = £38,400

Using the second formula:

    total contribution = (3,200 × £20) – (3,200 × £8) = £64,000 – £25,600 = £38,400

    annual profit = total contribution – fixed costs = £38,400 – £24,000 = £14,400

Breakeven analysis

Breakeven analysis is the study of the relationship between total costs and total revenue to identify the output at which a business breaks even (i.e. makes neither a profit nor a loss). A business can also use this to discover the effect of changes in output on its profit.

Breakeven output (quantity) is the level of output at which total sales revenue is equal to the total costs of production.

Breakeven analysis is based on the following assumptions:
- The selling price stays the same (e.g. £20 per unit).
- Fixed costs remain the same (e.g. £24,000).
- Variable costs vary in direct proportion to output (e.g. £8 per unit).
- Every unit of output that is produced is sold.

Calculating breakeven

The formula for calculating breakeven output is:

$$\text{breakeven output} = \frac{\text{fixed costs (£)}}{\text{contribution per unit (£)}}$$

If the price is £25 and variable costs are £13 per unit, each unit produced makes a contribution of £12 towards fixed costs or profit. If fixed costs are £48,000, then:

$$\frac{£48,000}{£25 - £13} = \frac{£48,000}{£12} = 4,000 \text{ units are needed to break even}$$

Breakeven charts

The diagram shows a breakeven chart based on the following data:
- selling price = £60 per unit
- variable costs = £20 per unit
- fixed costs = £400
- actual and maximum outputs = 15 units

The total cost line is drawn by adding fixed costs and variable costs at each level of output.

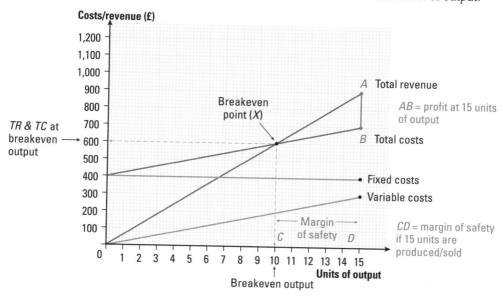

From the diagram it is possible to deduce:
- The breakeven point where total costs (*TC*) = total revenue (*TR*) (point *X*).
- The breakeven output (shown by the vertical dotted line drawn from point *X* to the x-axis). This is 10 units in this example.
- The sales revenue and total costs at the breakeven output (shown by the horizontal dotted line drawn from point *X* to the y-axis). This is £600 in this example.
- The profit made at every level of output (the vertical distance between *TR* and *TC*). At 15 units this is £900 – £700 = £200 (shown by the vertical distance between *A* and *B* in the diagram). At 10 units (the breakeven output) it is £600 – £600 = £0.
- The margin of safety — the difference between the actual output and the breakeven output. At 15 units of output this is 15 – 10 = 5 units (shown by the horizontal distance between *C* and *D* in the diagram.

Effects of cost and price changes

What happens to breakeven when variables such as fixed costs, variable costs and selling prices change?

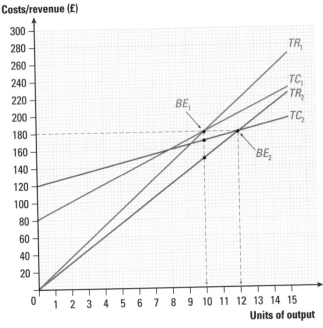

In this diagram, the original values are:
- selling price = £18 per unit
- variable costs = £10 per unit
- fixed costs = £80

For simplicity, only the total revenue and total cost lines are shown. TR_1 is the initial total revenue line. TC_1 is the initial total costs line. It starts at £80 (the level of fixed costs) and slopes upwards at a rate of £10 per unit (the variable costs per unit).

The lines TR_2 and TC_2 show the new lines caused by the following changes:
- selling price falls to £15 per unit
- variable costs fall to £5 per unit
- fixed costs increase to £120

The breakeven point where $TC = TR$ moves from BE_1 to BE_2.

The breakeven output rises from 10 units to 12 units.

The sales revenue and total costs at the breakeven output are £180 in both cases.

If 15 units are produced, the profit changes from £270 – £230 = £40 to £225 – £195 = £30.

At 15 units of output, the margin of safety was 15 – 10 = 5 units, but when breakeven output rises to 12 units, the margin of safety is 15 – 12 = 3 units.

The usefulness of breakeven analysis

The benefits of breakeven analysis are:
- A new firm can calculate how long it will take to reach the level of output needed to make a profit. This will help it to get financial support, such as a bank overdraft.
- It is a straightforward way for a start-up to discover whether its business plan is likely to succeed, financially.
- It can show a business its margin of safety. The business can calculate by how much sales can fall before it drops below the quantity needed to break even.
- It allows a firm to use 'what if?' analysis to show the different breakeven outputs and the changes in profit levels that might arise from changes in price, variable costs and fixed costs.
- It shows the different levels of profit arising from all of the possible levels of output.

However, the assumptions of breakeven analysis are not always true. It is also very difficult to predict costs and revenue.

Questions

1 State two examples of fixed costs.

....

2 State two examples of variable costs.

....

Answer questions 3 to 8, based on the following data:
- units of output = 800
- fixed costs = £6,000
- variable costs = £25 per unit
- selling price = £40 per unit

3 Calculate the contribution per unit.

4 Calculate the total contribution from 800 units.

5 Calculate the breakeven output.

6 How much profit/loss is made if all 800 units are sold?

7 How much profit/loss is made if only 300 units are sold?

8 What is the margin of safety if 800 units are sold?

9 Based on the following data:
- selling price = £8 per unit
- variable costs = £5 per unit
- fixed costs = £30

add the total revenue line, variable costs line, fixed costs line and total costs line to the blank breakeven chart on page 51.

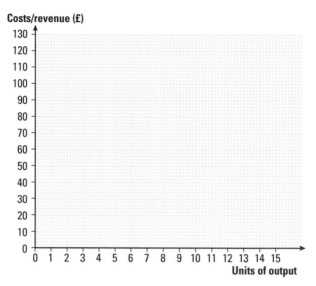

Costs/revenue (£)

Units of output

10 Label the breakeven point. Show the breakeven level of output. Show the profit level if 12 units of output are produced.

11 Show the new total costs line if variable costs fall to £3 per unit. Label the new breakeven point. Show the new breakeven quantity. Show the new profit level if 12 units are produced.

12 The breakeven chart below illustrates the original total revenue and total cost lines for a product (TR_1 and TC_1) and the lines arising from changes in price and costs (TR_2 and TC_2).

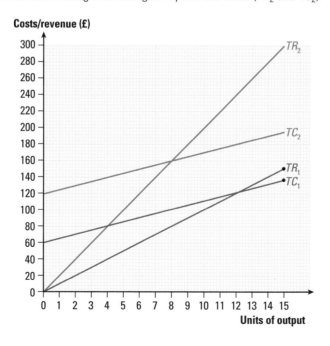

Costs/revenue (£)

Units of output

a Based on the original revenue and cost lines, TR_1 and TC_1, what is the breakeven output?

....

b What are the variable costs per unit?

....

c Based on the new revenue and cost lines, TR_2 and TC_2, what is the new breakeven output?

....

d What is the new selling price?

....

e What are the new fixed costs?

....

13 A plumber decides to move from Mansfield to Manchester in order to set up as a sole trader, having completed his apprenticeship and worked as an employee for 6 years. How useful is breakeven analysis likely to be in this situation?

....

....

....

....

....

....

....

....

....

....

....

....

Using cash-flow forecasting

The nature of cash flow

Cash flow is the amount of money flowing into and out of a business over a period of time.

Cash inflows are receipts of cash, typically arising from sales of items, payments by debtors, loans received, rent charged, sale of assets and interest received.

Cash outflows are payments of cash, typically arising from the purchase of items, payments to creditors, loans repaid or given, rental payments, purchase of assets and interest payments.

Net cash flow is the sum of cash inflows to an organisation minus the sum of cash outflows over a period of time.

Cash outflows normally take place before cash inflows. Typically a business's cash flow will follow these stages:
- purchase of materials = cash outflow
- transformation of inputs into outputs = cash outflow
- sale of outputs = cash inflow

It can be seen that there is a tendency for cash to flow out of a business before it flows back in. This means that a typical business might suffer cash-flow problems.

Cash-flow forecasting

Cash-flow forecasting is the process of estimating cash inflows and cash outflows over a period of time, usually for a period of 1 year.

A business can use a number of sources for its cash-flow forecasts:
- previous cash-flow forecasts
- consumer research
- study of similar businesses, such as competitors
- research into the level of resources needed
- banks and consultants

Potential problems in forecasting cash flow are:
- changes in the economy and consumer tastes
- inaccurate market research
- actions of competitors

The structure of a cash-flow forecast

The details of cash-flow forecasts vary according to the type of business. However, the key items in constructing a cash-flow forecast are as follows:
- **Cash inflows.** This item usually contains details of income from sales but also includes cash from items such as rent received, money borrowed in the form of loans and sale of assets.
- **Cash outflows.** Examples are purchase of raw materials, wages and rent. A business must also recognise one-off payments, such as for a new vehicle.

- **Net cash flow.** The formula for net cash flow is:

  net cash flow = cash inflows – cash outflows

- **Opening balance and closing balance.** A company's original cash holding at the start of a period is its opening balance. The formula for closing balance is:

  closing cash balance = opening cash balance + net cash flow

Why do businesses forecast cash flow?

The main reasons for forecasting cash flow are to:
- identify potential cash-flow problems in advance
- guide the firm towards appropriate action by highlighting potential problems
- make sure that there is sufficient cash available to make any necessary payments
- provide evidence in support of financial assistance (such as a bank overdraft)
- avoid the possibility of the company being forced out of business (into liquidation)
- identify the possibility of holding too much cash (which may reduce profitability)

Questions

1 Explain the meaning of the term 'cash-flow forecast'.

....

....

....

2 Identify two different examples of cash inflows.

....

....

3 Identify three different sources of information for a cash-flow forecast.

....

....

....

4 Identify two different examples of cash outflows.

....

....

5 Explain two reasons why an organisation should prepare a cash-flow forecast.

....

....

....

....

6 Explain two problems that a firm might have when trying to predict its cash flow.

....

....

....

....

....

....

7 Complete the cash-flow forecast in the table based on the following data:
  - Sales income is expected to be £36,000 in quarter 1 and £40,000 in quarter 2.
  - Raw materials will cost 25% of the forecast sales income in each quarter.
  - Wages will be £10,700 per quarter.
  - 'Other costs' will be £12,200 in quarter 1 and £3,800 in quarter 2.

Cash inflows and cash outflows for Albert Breeze, quarters 1 and 2

	Quarter 1	**Quarter 2**
Opening balance	6,800	
Sales income/total inflows		
Raw materials		
Wages		
Other costs		
Total outflows		
Net quarterly balance (or flow)		
Closing balance		

Setting budgets

Types of budget

A **budget** is an agreed plan establishing, in numerical or financial terms, the policy to be pursued and the anticipated outcomes of that policy. There are three main types of budget:

- **Income budget.** This shows the agreed, planned income of a business (or division of a business) over a period of time. It may also be described as a **revenue budget** or **sales budget**.
- **Expenditure budget.** This shows the agreed, planned expenditure of a business (or division of a business) over a period of time. Costs that may be found in an expenditure budget include raw materials, wages, purchases of machinery and vehicles, and rent paid.
- **Profit budget.** This shows the agreed, planned profit of a business (or division of a business) over a period of time.

The process of setting a budget

Stage 1: Set objectives.
Stage 2: Carry out market research to discover probable sales and the market price.
Stage 3: Carry out research into costs, based on the sales volume expected.
Stage 4: Complete the sales (income) budget and use it to estimate output.
Stage 5: Construct the expenditure budget.
Stage 6: Combine stages 4 and 5 to create an overall profit budget.
Stage 7: Managers in each area of the business draw up divisional or departmental budgets.
Stage 8: Summarise these detailed budgets in the master budget.

The following tables are examples of completed income, expenditure and profit budgets.

Income budget for Jules Ltd, 2010

Source of income	Income (£)
Sales of newspapers	32,000
Sales of magazines	22,000
Confectionery sales	98,000
Total income	**152,000**

Expenditure budget for Jules Ltd, 2010

Item of expenditure	Expenditure (£)
Purchases of newspapers	22,000
Purchases of magazines	11,000
Purchases of confectionery	46,000
Labour costs	23,000
Rent	6,000
Other costs	10,000
Total expenditure	**118,000**

Profit budget for Jules Ltd, 2010	Income/expenditure	£
	Total income	152,000
	Total expenditure	118,000
	Budgeted profit	**34,000**

Methods of setting a budget

The main methods of setting a budget are:
- budgeting according to company objectives
- budgeting according to competitors' spending
- setting the budget as a percentage of sales revenue
- zero budgeting/budgeting based on expected outcomes
- budgeting according to last year's budget allocation

Reasons for setting budgets

The main reasons for setting budgets are to:
- gain financial support from investors
- ensure that a business does not overspend
- establish priorities
- encourage delegation and responsibility, and motivate staff
- assign responsibility
- improve efficiency

Problems of setting budgets

The main problems with budgets are:
- Managers may not know enough about the division or department to know what is required.
- Gathering information can be costly.
- There may be unforeseen changes, such as changes in tastes or suppliers.
- The level of inflation (price rises) is not easy to predict.
- Budgets may be imposed rather than agreed.
- Setting a budget can be time consuming.

Questions

1 What is meant by the term 'budget'?

2 Describe the stages involved in setting a budget.

3 Explain three reasons why a sole trader thinking of setting up a computer repair business would find it helpful to set budgets.

4 What are the main difficulties facing the owner of a new computer repair business when trying to plan a budget?

5 Tahla is planning to set up a computer repair business and has estimated the following figures for her first year of trading. Using the templates provided, complete the income budget, expenditure budget and profit budget for her first year of trading.
  - Average price charged for computer repairs: £80
  - Budgeted number of repairs per year: 650
  - Sales of software to customers: 300 units at an average price of £30
  - Sales of hardware: 70 units at average price of £100
  - Purchases of equipment and components: £12,500
  - Purchases of hardware and software: £8,000
  - Wages, rent and other costs: £22,700

Annual income budget for Tahla's computer repair business

Source of income	Average price (£)	Number	Total (£)
Total			

Annual expenditure budget for Tahla's computer repair business

Item of expenditure	Expenditure (£)
Total	

Annual profit budget for Tahla's computer repair business

Income/expenditure	£
Income	
Expenditure	
Profit	

6 Tahla is currently working in a secure job in which she earns £25,000 a year. On the basis of the projected budgets, advise her on whether her start-up business is worthwhile financially.

....

....

....

....

....

....

7 Analyse two other factors that Tahla should consider before making a decision on whether to set up her new business or remain in her current job.

....

....

....

....

....

....

....

....

....

Assessing business start-ups

Objectives of business start-ups

The objectives of business start-ups include to:
- be independent and gain more freedom at work
- make money
- sustain a going concern such as a family business and provide employment for the local community, sometimes in the form of social enterprises

Assessing the business idea and/or plan

Issues to consider include:
- what the business's objectives are
- which product/service to provide and whether it can be provided profitably
- customers' needs and wants, and which market segment to target
- the possibility of competition and an appropriate pricing and selling strategy
- finance and the time between start-up and reaching breakeven
- who will be involved, what they will be doing, and what expertise and experience they have
- the risks involved

Questions to consider include:
- Is there anything special about the product that would make it appeal to consumers?
- Could the product compete successfully with similar products on the market?

Why start-ups can be risky and why they may fail

Potential problems that business start-ups might encounter can be categorised as follows:
- **finance** — raising funds, problems of cash flow, uncertainty about costs
- **marketing** — deciding on the product, forecasting demand, deciding on the target market, conducting market research, deciding on price and advertising and promotion
- **operations** — finding suitable premises, deciding on location and production methods, identifying reliable sources of supply, new technology
- **personnel and the organisation** — deciding on recruitment and selection strategies, providing training, deciding on the most effective organisational structure, quality of management and the skills needed to run a business
- **external factors** — complying with regulations, the impact of macro-economic policies, the competitive environment in which the business operates
- **personal problems** — suitability for self-employment, how the owner will provide cover for illness, what the opportunity cost of this business start-up is

In addition, when a business has been running for some time, other problems can cause business failure, including:
- unexpected changes in demand for the product or service
- unexpected changes in costs
- delays and unavailability of supplies

Raising finance

As a new business has no 'track record', it is seen as much more of a risk than an established business. Banks provide most of the external funds for small business start-ups, mainly in the form of loans and overdrafts. They do, however, require collateral or security. Lack of finance may affect a business as follows:

- slow the growth of the business
- threaten the survival of the business
- affect the productivity of the business
- affect the ability of the business to invest (e.g. in new machinery or premises)
- take up management time in seeking sources of finance
- raise costs, because a lack of finance may mean the business is not operating efficiently

Cash-flow problems

Even firms that are profitable sometimes find it impossible to continue trading because they are unable to meet their current debts. It is essential for a business to ensure that it has enough cash available for its working capital needs. In order to do this, a cash-flow forecast is prepared. This shows the expected variation in working capital needs over a period of time and should indicate when overdraft facilities will be needed to cover any shortfalls.

Competition and the difficulties of building a customer base

The success of a business start-up will be determined by its ability to attract and retain its customers. To do this it will have to offer something more than any of its competitors. Factors to consider when trying to encourage customer loyalty include:

- providing customers with service that is efficient and meets their expectations
- providing good after-sales service and dealing effectively with complaints
- understanding customers' buying habits and ensuring good stock and staff availability
- ensuring that contact between customers and staff is always friendly and efficient

Regulations and 'red tape'

Small businesses often complain about the difficulties they encounter in dealing with 'red tape'. This usually refers to the many legal requirements facing a business, including those relating to employment, health and safety, consumer protection and environmental protection as well as the requirements relating to taxation and other financial issues.

Questions

1 State three possible objectives for a business start-up.

2 Explain three factors that need to be considered when assessing the likely success of a business idea.

....

....

....

....

....

....

3 Using examples to illustrate, explain why a business might fail as a result of unexpected changes in demand and in costs.

....

....

....

....

4 Using examples to illustrate, explain why a business might fail as a result of delays in, or the unavailability of, certain supplies.

....

....

....

....

5 Explain two reasons why business start-ups find raising finance difficult.

....

....

....

....

6 Some businesses fail despite being profitable. Why?

....

....

....

....

7 Why should a business start-up give careful thought to its competitors?

8 How can a new business ensure that it builds a solid customer base?

9 Given that all firms are subject to regulation and legislation, why does 'red tape' create particular problems for small business start-ups?

10 Assess the most likely reasons for a small business to fail.